GRAPHIC SCIENCE

THE **ILLUMINATING WORLD** OF

LIGHT

WITH
SUPER SCIENTIST

Emily Sohn

illustrated by Nick Derington

Raintree

www.raintreepublishers.co.uk
Visit our website to find out
more information about
Raintree books.

To order:
☎ Phone +44 (0) 1865 888066
🖹 Fax +44 (0) 1865 314091
🖳 Visit www.raintreepublishers.co.uk

Raintree is an imprint of Capstone Global Library Limited, a company incorporated in England and
Wales having its registered office at 7 Pilgrim Street, London EC4V 6LB
Registered company number: 6695882

Text © Capstone Press 2008
First published by Capstone Press in 2008
First published in hardback in the United Kingdom by Capstone Global Library in 2010
First published in paperback in the United Kingdom by Capstone Global Library in 2011
The moral rights of the proprietor have been asserted.

ISBN 978 1 4062 1458 1 (hardback)   ISBN 978 1 4062 1474 1 (paperback)
14 13 12 11 10   15 14 13 12 11

British Library Cataloguing in Publication Data
Sohn, Emily
Light. -- (Graphic science)
535-dc22
A full catalogue record for this book is available from the British Library.

Art Director and Designer: Bob Lentz
Cover Artist: Tod Smith
UK Editor: Diyan Leake
UK Production: Alison Parsons
Originated by Capstone Global Library
Printed and bound in China by South China Printing Company Limited

Acknowledgements
The publisher would like to thank the following for permission to reproduce copyright material:
iStockphoto p. 23; Shutterstock p. 13 (Jo-Hanna Wienert)

CONTENTS

SECTION 1

I SEE THE LIGHT ---------------------- 4

SECTION 2

WHAT LIGHT CAN DO -------------- 10

SECTION 3

WHAT WE CAN DO WITH LIGHT --- 18

SECTION 4

ENERGY CONVERSION ----------- 24

More about light and Max Axiom 28–29
Glossary.. 30
Find out more... 31
Index 32

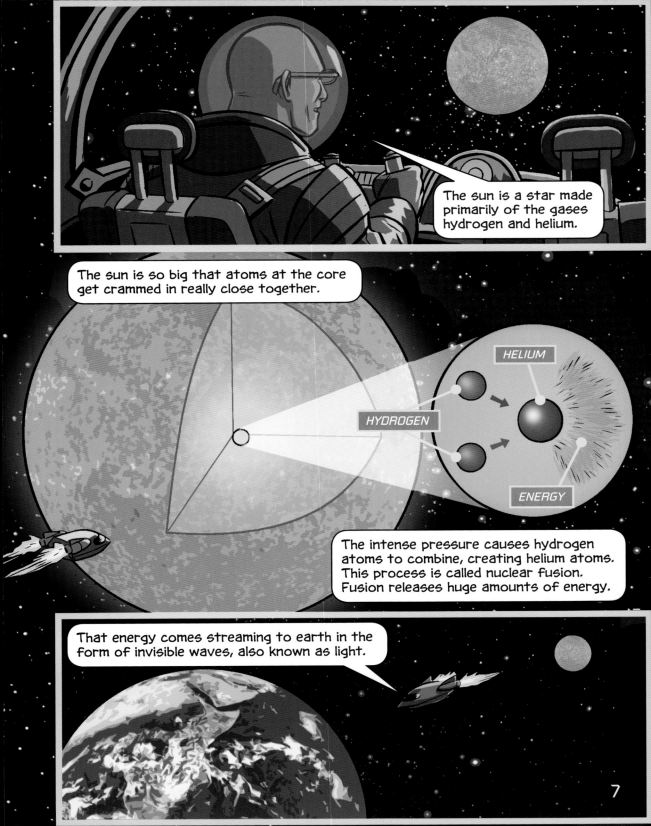

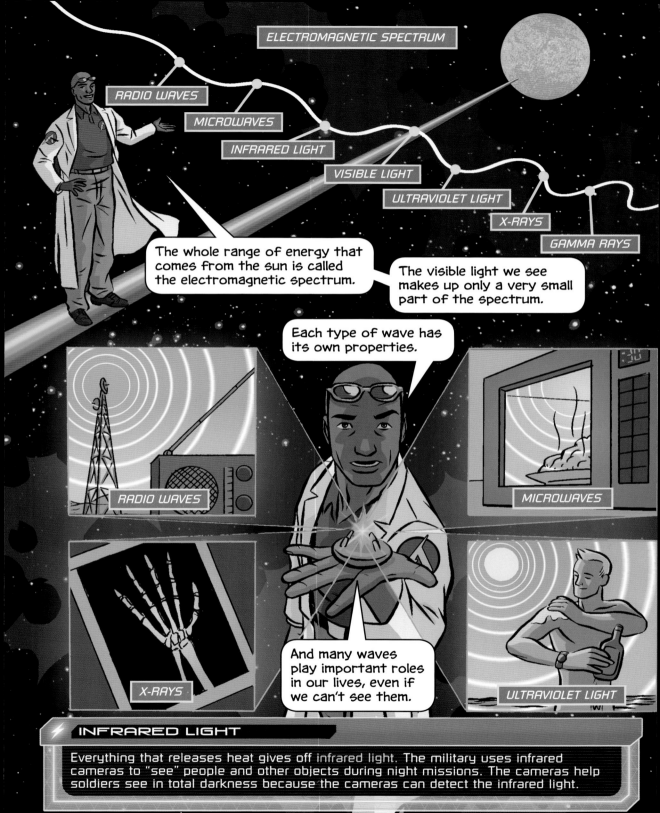

You probably think of sunlight as white and bright.

But hidden inside visible light are all the colours of the rainbow.

This clear piece of glass is a prism. Like the water droplets from the sprinkler, it makes rainbows too.

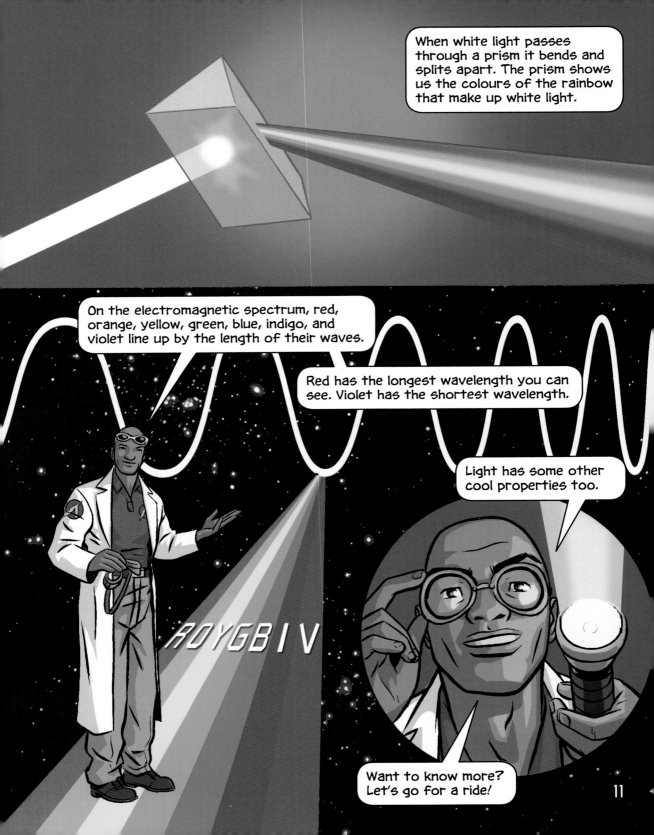

If you could ride a beam of light, you'd be the fastest person on earth.

Light moves about 299,300 kilometres, or 186,000 miles, a second.

Nothing moves faster. Yee haw!

LIGHT YEARS

The distance light travels in a year is called a light year. One light year equals 10 trillion kiiometres (6.2 trillion miles). The closest star to earth, after the sun, is 4.3 light years away.

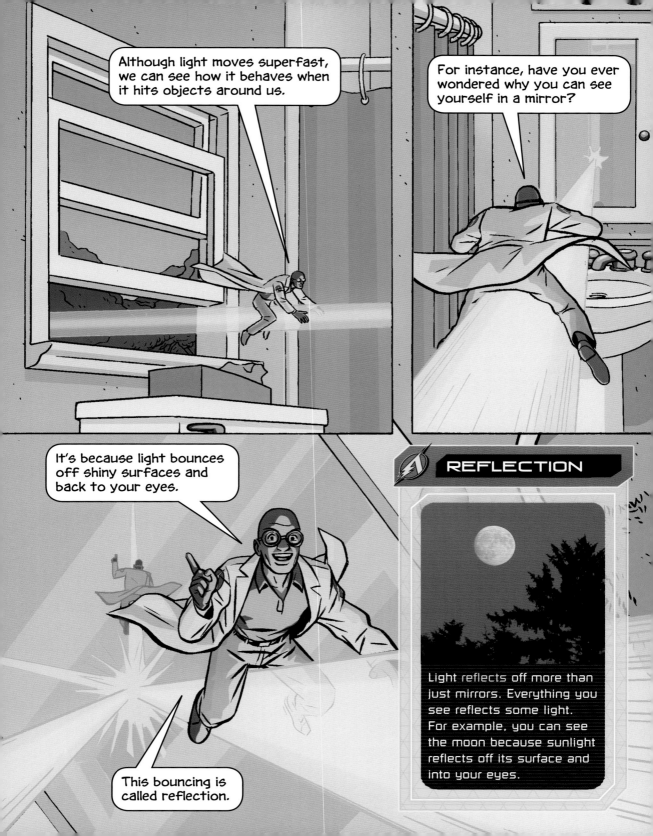

14

Because opaque objects block light, we see shadows, or dark spots, behind them.

Of course, not all objects are completely transparent or totally opaque.

Some objects are translucent. For example, this stained glass window lets some light through, but we can't see through it to the other side.

Look, Mum! That's Max Axiom. He visited my school during the science lesson last week.

It's good to see you again, Carla. May I borrow one of your drinks for a moment?

Sure. Why?

Because it's the perfect example of refracting light.

Have you ever noticed that objects look distorted when you put them in a glass of water?

You're right!

It looks like the straw is broken!

But you know that it's not. It's an optical illusion.

One of the most important things we do with light is see.

Let's take a look at how our eyes use light.

The human eye is only about 2.5 centimetres tall and 2.5 centimetres wide, but it's a complicated organ.

CORNEA

PUPIL

Light comes in through the cornea and travels to the pupil.

The pupil changes size to let in more or less light, depending on how bright it is outside.

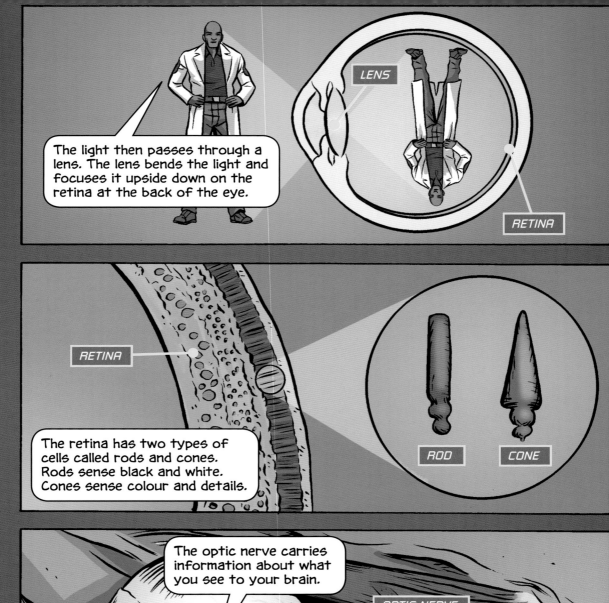

The light then passes through a lens. The lens bends the light and focuses it upside down on the retina at the back of the eye.

LENS

RETINA

RETINA

The retina has two types of cells called rods and cones. Rods sense black and white. Cones sense colour and details.

ROD

CONE

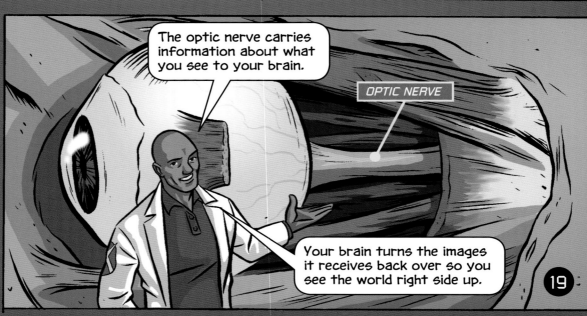

The optic nerve carries information about what you see to your brain.

OPTIC NERVE

Your brain turns the images it receives back over so you see the world right side up.

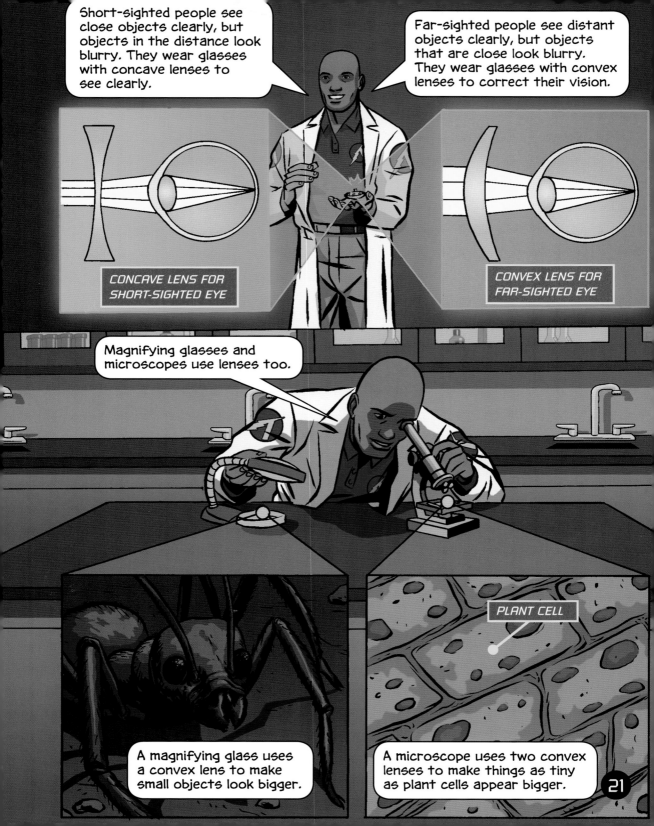

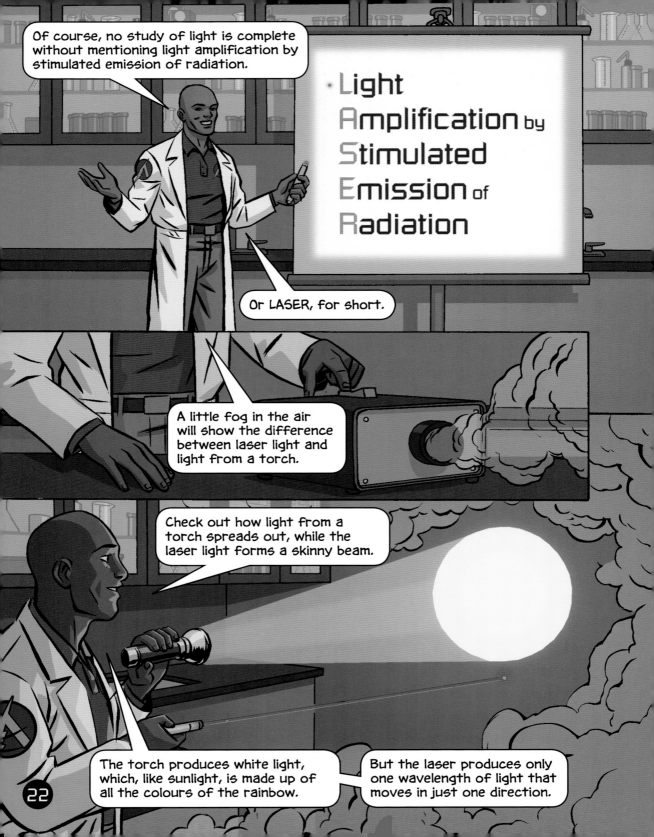

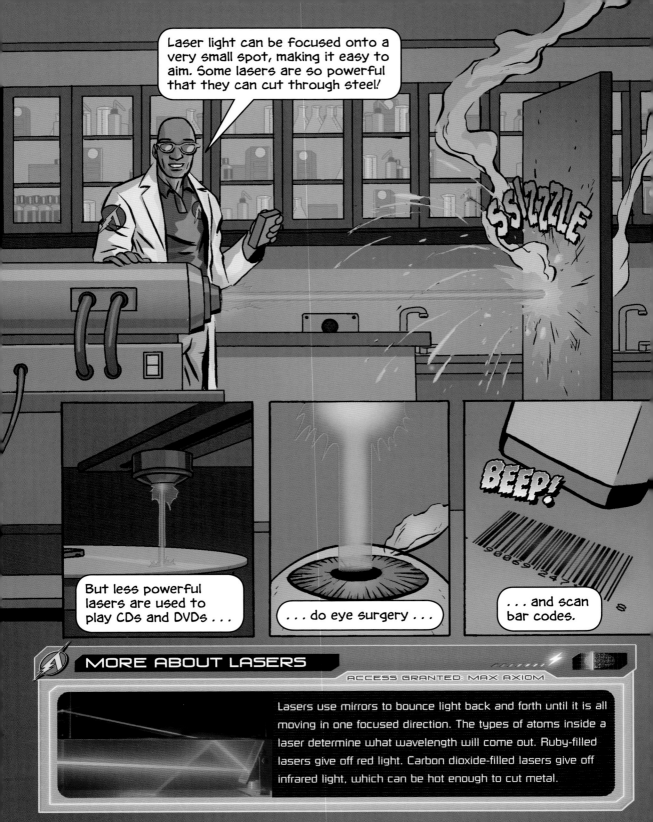

MORE ABOUT LIGHT

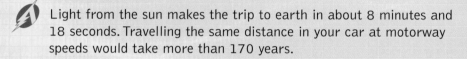

Light from the sun makes the trip to earth in about 8 minutes and 18 seconds. Travelling the same distance in your car at motorway speeds would take more than 170 years.

Light changes speeds when it passes from one material to another. When light passes from air to water, it slows down to about 225,000 kilometres (139,800 miles) per second.

The colour of your T-shirt on a sunny, summer day can make a big difference in how hot you feel. Darker colours absorb more light than lighter colours. To stay cooler, wear a white T-shirt on a sunny day because it reflects more light than a darker shirt.

Only 10 percent of the energy used by a regular incandescent lightbulb is changed into visible light. The rest of the energy is wasted as heat.

Telescopes use lenses or mirrors to capture the little bits of light that come to earth from stars, planets, and galaxies in space. The Hubble Space Telescope has allowed us to see galaxies more than 12 billion light years away.

Human eyes can sense light only within the visible wavelengths on the electromagnetic spectrum. Some animals see the world in a completely different way. Rattlesnakes have sensory pits that detect infrared light. Bees see ultraviolet light.

Moonbows are rainbows that form at night. These faint rainbows form when raindrops refract light reflecting off the moon. When moonlight refracts off ice crystals in the atmosphere, bright halos called moon dogs form around the moon.

 Solar energy powers satellites and spacecraft orbiting earth. The International Space Station's huge solar panels turn sunlight into electricity, light, and heat for the astronauts living and working on the spacecraft.

MORE ABOUT

SUPER SCIENTIST

Real name: Maxwell Axiom
Height: 1.86 m (6 ft 1 in.)
Weight: 87 kg (13 st. 10 lb.)
Eyes: Brown   Hair: None

Super capabilities: Super intelligence; able to shrink to the size of an atom; sunglasses give X-ray vision; lab coat allows for travel through time and space.

Origin: Since birth, Max Axiom seemed destined for greatness. His mother, a marine biologist, taught her son about the mysteries of the sea. His father, a nuclear physicist and volunteer park warden, showed Max the wonders of the earth and sky.

One day, while Max was hiking in the hills, a megacharged lightning bolt struck him with blinding fury. When he awoke, he discovered a new-found energy and set out to learn as much about science as possible. He travelled the globe studying every aspect of the subject. Then he was ready to share his knowledge and new identity with the world. He had become Max Axiom, Super Scientist.

GLOSSARY

atom smallest form of any element

concave hollow and curved, like the inside of a bowl

convex curved outward, like the outside of a ball

energy ability to do work, such as moving things or giving heat or light

fusion joining together of objects caused by heating. The sun creates its energy with the process of fusion.

infrared light light that produces heat. Humans cannot see infrared light.

laser thin, intense, high-energy beam of light

opaque blocks light

reflection change in direction of light bouncing off a surface

refract bend light at an angle as it passes through a substance

translucent lets light pass through, but is not transparent. Frosted and stained glass are translucent.

transparent lets light through

ultraviolet light an invisible form of light that can cause sunburns

wavelength distance between two peaks of a wave

FIND OUT MORE

Books

Electricity: Turn It On!, Wendy Sadler (Raintree, 2005)

Experiments with Light, Rachel Lynette (Heinemann Library, 2008)

Fossil Fuels and Biofuels, Elizabeth Raum (Heinemann Library, 2008)

Light (Tabletop Scientist series), Steve Parker (Heinemann Library, 2005)

The Story Behind Electricity, Sean Price (Heinemann Library, 2009)

Voyage of a Light Beam, Andrew Solway (Raintree, 2005)

Website

www.bbc.co.uk/schools/ks2bitesize
Click on "Science" and then "Physical processes" for activities and quizzes on topics such as "Light and dark" and "Light and shadows"

http://news.bbc/co.uk/cbbcnews
Enter "light" in the Search field to find out how this topic has been in the news.

atoms, 7, 23, 26

colours, 10–11, 19, 22, 28

electricity, 25, 26, 27, 29
electromagnetic spectrum, 9,
    11, 28
energy, 6, 7, 8, 9, 24, 25, 27,
    28, 29
eyes, 13, 17, 18, 19, 20, 23, 28

glasses, 20–21

heat, 9, 24, 25, 27, 28, 29

infrared light, 9, 23, 28

lasers, 22, 23
lenses, 19, 20–21, 28
lightbulbs, 26, 28
lightning, 4
light years, 12, 28

magnifying glasses, 21
microscopes, 21
mirrors, 13, 23, 28
moon, 13, 29
moonbows, 29
moon dogs, 29

nuclear fusion, 7

opaque objects, 14, 15

photosynthesis, 6
prisms, 10, 11

rainbows, 5, 10, 11, 22, 29
reflection, 13, 17, 23, 28
refraction, 16–17, 29

shadows, 15
solar energy, 24–25, 29
speed of light, 12, 17, 28
sunlight, 6–7, 8, 10, 13, 22, 25,
    26, 28, 29

telescopes, 28
translucent objects, 15
transparent objects, 14, 15, 17

ultraviolet light, 9, 28

visible light, 9, 10, 28

wavelengths, 8, 11, 22, 23, 28